NON-STOP-ROCK'N'ROLL VOODOO ACTION!!!

VINCE RAY

SUFFOLK AND WATT

Vice Ray

Non-stop Rock 'n' Roll Voodoo Action
First published in Great Britain in 2005

SUFFOLK AND WATT

London

Please send all corospondence to
8 John's Terrace, East Croydon,
Surrey, CRO 6TD
ENGLAND
www.suffolkandwatt.com

ISBN: 0-9545985-1-2

www.vinceray.com
www.vincentrazorbacks.com

Design: Mighty Fine Design, London, England
www.mightyfine.co.uk

Printed in England by Sarum Colourview
Many thanks to the whip-master Nicky Forbes

REQUIEM FOR A
$PLEEN

What you are about to read is based on a true story

by Billy Chainsaw

t was a night like any other on the rock 'n' roll road to ruin and damnation. Having just pulverised the patrons of The Nun and Two Goats pub into sweat and booze-soaked submission, The Vincent Razorbacks were en route to their next engagement. The R-backs were in the drummer's battered but souped-up hearse, and their head honcho, Vincent – AKA Vince Ray, was behind the wheel of the equipment van. The reason for the parting of their ways was simple: Monsieur Ray had cajoled bad-ass scribe Billy Chainsaw into doing an interview for his new book. Yes, the one you now clutch in your claws. Having turned left at the bum-hole of humanity known as Uttoxeter, our delirious duo found themselves careering down deserted country lanes, as hungry as hell and twice as thirsty. Suddenly, a short way up ahead, a light broke through the backwoods blackness. "Pub!" screamed Chainsaw… and what do you know, it was.

Vince pulled into the driveway, shook his head despairingly and muttered, "Do you really expect me to walk into a pub called The Deliverance?" "What! You think they're going to ask you to drop your britches and squeal like a pig?" chuckled Chainsaw. "Exactly!" replied Vince, his face the colour of a whore's drawers. "Don't be daft," said Chainsaw, still chuckling. "It's not going

to happen, because A: we've got tattoos which makes us hard and B: being better looking than their sexual partners, human or otherwise, we're just not their type." Reassured, Vince slapped Chainsaw on the back, opened the door to the pub and marched straight up to the bar. "What's your poison, Sir?" asked a Byron-esque looking refuge from a Hammer Horror flick. "Any chance of a couple of Martinis?" said Vince, with an expectant smile. "As much as I'd like to Sir, the locals don't drink such things…but can I tempt you with the speciality of the house instead?" "Absolutely," agreed Chainsaw over Vince's shoulder. The barman pulled the boys two pints of what appeared to be dark beer, although they were frothing like a lab experiment, all bubbles and smoke. "Here Chain, these look great!" declared Vince. Chainsaw didn't look quite so convinced and piped up, "I don't suppose there's any chance of a spot of nosebag at this late hour is there?" "Nosebag, Sir?" "The ingrate means food," explained Vince, before taking a swig of his drink. "Ah, I see," said the barman, with a knowing nod. "Well, chef's gone for the night, but I'm sure we can rustle up a couple of cheese sandwiches, a plate of pickles and some crisps… would that be to Sirs' liking?" The chaps nodded silently, their mouths clamped on their glasses. "Then take a seat and I'll have our waitress bring you your food in a moment." Vince and Chainsaw sat with their backs to the wall surveying their surroundings. The Deliverance looked like every other ukulele-playing, inbred yokel watering hole they'd ever been in, except for one thing; for once, the locals hadn't greeted them with Paddington Bear hard stares, slights on their manhood and threats on their lives. It was a fact that, had they not been gagging for sustenance, the boys would have realised that was in itself weird.

"You want to start the interview then?" asked Chainsaw, pointing at his tape-recorder. "Yep, let's go" replied Vince. "Okay Mr Ray…how come you've never featured fish in your artwork?" "I hate the little fuckers, I've got a big fish complex! The closest I've come to drawing a fish is a Nazi mermaid. She was Hitler's secret weapon and she rocked! As for the taste of fish… if God had meant us to eat sushi, why did he make it taste like shite? I can manage the odd fish finger, but it has to be odd… in fact I'm much fonder of pickled eggs." "Mmm… pickled eggs." Just then, a buxom waitress arrived with their food and would you believe it, the pickle selection contained two eggs. "Thanks, Darling," said Vince, before devouring one of the eggs whole. Chainsaw did the same, took a swig of beer and continued, "What about Japanese schoolgirls? I don't recall having seen one of those mischievous minxes in any of your pictures." "That's a major sore point," declared Vince. "I was once asked to take a photo of a group of the oriental sweethearts in Trafalgar Square. However, the camera they handed me looked so cool I took off with it… big mistake! It turned out that a few of them were nifty at the old martial arts, so when they caught me, they sat on my head and gave me a good kicking!" "Wow! I wish a Japanese schoolgirl would sit on my face!" said Chainsaw, now looking somewhat bleary eyed. "It's not fucking funny!" shouted Vince. "Those pleated skirts caused such nasty chaffing, the very thought of attempting to draw one of the evil bitches makes parts of my body throb… and not in a sex related way either!"

By now Chainsaw was grinning so wide it looked like his face would split. "Fuck me Vince, old Byron weren't kidding… this is bloody strong stuff" "No shit Sherlock, next question." "Okay, what's the most hideous nightmare you've ever had?" Without pause for thought, Vince replied, "I once dreamt that you and me were in this weird pub and… fuckin' hell, that pickled egg just winked at me!" "What? Where?" "Over there in that jar on the bar!" Chainsaw looked but saw no winking egg. However, what he did see was that the barman, he'd branded Byron, was flashing a pair of pearly white fangs, and he cast no reflection in the mirror behind him. Chain swiftly turned back to face Vince and, not wishing to be declared a deranged dickwad, continued his questioning. "You've never drawn any ants… they were favoured by the surrealist likes of Salvador Dali, so why not you?" "Fuckit, you've got me there, Chain. But, while I may have never drawn one, I ate some once in a chocolate bar from Singapore. I was drunk at a party and playing a forfeit game – I can't tell you what else I ate. Hang on a minute though… back in the days when I worked on sex comics I was going to do a story called 'Honey I Shrunk My Penis'. It was about a guy experimenting with a chemistry set in his garden shed who was trying to en-

large his manhood, but he gets the formula wrong and shrinks himself to the size of a peanut. I was looking forward to drawing him running through giant blades of grass as he's being chased by female insects like a wasp woman, a beetle girl, a mistress moth and an auntie ant with a big slipper!" Suddenly, someone shouted, "Size of a mouse!" Vince and Chainsaw looked to their left just in time to see a guy disappear in a puff of smoke, only to reappear seconds later on top of his table, no bigger than a newborn rodent. He casually walked over to an ashtray filled with

beer, dived into it and did the breast-stroke in an anti-clockwise direction until he'd drank the boozy contents. Then he rolled over onto his back, burped, farted and began returning to his full-sized form. Unfortunately, as he did so, he went crashing off the table and into the open jaws of a passing alligator. Half a dozen bright green poodles trotted behind the scaly beast, no doubt hoping for a few tasty scraps.

"It's fucking brilliant in here!" declared Chainsaw, thinking there was nothing so unusual about what they'd just witnessed. But, obviously inspired by the ravenous pooches, then asked Vince, "Have you ever drawn two dogs rutting?" "No, I can't say I've ever done doggies getting it on," he replied, his eyes spinning wildly. "The nearest I ever got to depicting animal sex was with a bestiality design I did for a punk band called the Pork Dukes. It was of a pig holding a knife and fork about to tuck into a woman's ass while he was rutting away at her. The Pork Dukes derived great pleasure from being politically incorrect – and I still wear that t-shirt with pride!" "You dirty cunt!" said Chainsaw, violently tugging Vince's right cheek. "So, what's the most erotic dream you've ever had then?" "Well… the last time I fell asleep was in 1987 for, I think, about 20 minutes. I dreamt I was in a graveyard noshing a kebab… a voodoo kebab of course. Can you still get those?" "Get on with it!" howled Chainsaw, whose chin suddenly hit the table at the sight of the Creature from the Black Lagoon sharing a basket of scampi and chips with Frankenstein's monster. "Suddenly, the kebab sprouted two legs and the biggest pair of breasts I've ever seen. Then a pair of googly eyes popped out of its head, followed by a humongous tongue that wrapped itself around me and yanked and yanked until my head came off and dropped inside its mouth! To top it all off, I was wearing one of those cute, pleated, Japanese schoolgirl skirts. I swear – FUCK! I haven't been able to get a wink of sleep since that damn dream. Talking of winking… I think that pickled egg really fancies me!"

Even before Chainsaw turned to look, he knew that this time there would be a winking pickled egg… and there was, accompanied by a plate of pork scratchings that had suddenly sprouted snouts and started oinking the theme tune from The Twilight Zone. "I bet Rod Serling would have quit smoking to spend a night in here," said Chainsaw, waving his arms like a conductor on crystal-meth. He continued: "Well that dream wasn't particularly sexy, so, sticking with my favourite three letter word…describe your most humiliating sexual experience." "All sexual experiences are humiliating," Vince informed him. "It's got to be one of God's favourite jokes. I'm sure he pisses himself laughing every time he peeks over a cloud and sees my skinny ass wriggling around. I remember once having sex in a mirrored-room. You know what it's like…" "Indeed I do not… but I do know that I've suddenly developed x-ray vision and that waitress who served us earlier has a shaved snatch!" "No shit?" "No shit, just snatch! But what about your spotty ass in a mirrored-room?" "Oh yeah… I guess you hope that when you look in the mirrors you'll see some sexual athlete, a kind of he-man pumping away… but instead all I saw was a little, pink, sweaty chap looking like his brain was about to explode. He looked shit, but I looked great!" Just then, the waitress turned to reveal a beautiful bare arse, then promptly vanished through a wall. Chainsaw simply let out a deafening peal of laughter and steamed back into inquisitor mode. "You mentioned God just then… how come you've never drawn his son, Jesus?" "It's funny how I draw the devil so often, yet I believe in neither him, God nor any kind of spiritual dimension. When I die, if it turns out that they DO exist, I hope you'll all help me give both of the cocksuckers the beating they deserve. But back to your question, I once did a design where Jesus was being strangled by a devil girl with a pointy-tail and next to her was a nun strangling Satan with a rosary – just to get the balance right. Personally, I'm sure all that kind of imagery and iconography is man made and that, as an artist you explore that belief system. I do go around churches quite a lot though, and not just to hang around the graveyards either. I love the architecture and religious paintings. Every time I do so though, I can't help thinking to myself…if Jesus had died in an electric chair, would Christians wear little gold electric chairs around their necks instead of crosses? And what about Joseph…his wife told him she got fucked by the Holy Ghost – and he believed it!"

"Whoa… controversial stuff!" declared Chainsaw. "But not as controversial as the Bride of Frankenstein giving the Wolfman a blow-job over there by the bar-billiards table!"

Suddenly, Vince discovered his neck had become rubberised and as he craned to catch a glimpse of Universal's finest in oral intercourse, he felt it stretch until he was able to get close enough to smell old Wolfie's sweaty nads. "Go Baby, go!" he yelled, only to get a back-hander from the Bride that was so violent, it snapped his neck back into place and straight into Chain's next question. "What a fucking clown you can be sometimes Mr Ray!" "How dare you, you, you cadaverous cad… cadaver you… I fucking hate clowns!" "Is that why you've never drawn one of those either?" "Ah but that's where you're wrong Mr Sparkle Motion Smarty Pants! Because there's an ear-plug-stretcher design I did for Wildcat that includes an evil clown face. It's funny that people have only recently sussed out that clowns are actually pretty scary characters and started portraying them that way. Maybe I should become a clown… 'Hey kids, it's Uncle Vince!' – I'm pretty good at twisting dogs into balloon shapes!" "Dogs into balloon shapes… you think that's such a cool trick? It's nowhere near as awesome as that shirt and tie dancing on top of that table," suggested Chainsaw, twisting Vince's head almost clean off his neck so that he could see it. "That's not just a shirt and tie, you twat!" "Well it sure as hell looks that way to me!" 'Wanker! That's the Invisible Man…and by the look of things, he's gone commando!" "I bet he never gets caught masturbating – did you Vince?" "I'm not sure…when I was still living with my parents, I once opened my eyes after successfully choking the chicken, to discover a steaming cup of tea on the bedside table. So I guess the answer is a big, er… maybe." "Did you have a porn stash

when you were still at home?" "Back then I guess all that kinda stuff started for most guys when they discovered the underwear section of their mum's catalogues. I wonder how many minds have been warped by Cross-Your-Heart bras and giant girdles? That's probably why I'm not a thong man, they're only good for cleaning between your teeth. But I digress… I stole the first jazz-mag I owned and stashed it in the garden shed. It had the rather subtle title of Skirt! My granddad found it and, just for a joke, used it to line the bottom of his budgie cage."

Hypnotised, not by Vince's words, but by the fact that a flock of miniature vultures were flying around the rocker's head in the formation of a bizarre feathery halo, Chainsaw was abruptly snapped from his reverie by someone shouting – "Duck!" He immediately screamed back, "They're vultures, not ducks!" only to have Vince slam his face into the table as a poisonous dart whizzed past the pair of them. "What the…?" asked Chainsaw, peeling the remains of a cheese sandwich from his left cheek.

"Sorry, Sir," said Byron the vampire barman, as he hovered above Vince and Chain's table. "The blow-dart players aren't renowned for their accuracy since they got their heads shrunk for losing to the witchdoctors in the regional finals. Can I get you both another drink?" Although they were smashed out of their skulls, the chaps nodded in acceptance of Byron's offer and Chainsaw spluttered, "Drink… I love drinking…do you prefer drink or drugs Vince?" "The great man Lux Interior once said 'All You need Is Enough Drugs'… but me, I'm more fond of beer these days. In fact that's the only body modification that interests me." "What the fuck's that got to do with body modification you bloody mong?" "Well you know how people stretch their ears and pierce their noses and stuff?" "Yeah…and?" "I just stretch my stomach as much as possible. I'm still fond of the odd Martini though, but like my fish fingers, it has to be odd… which means with a pickled egg instead of the traditional olive. Shit! We're back to that pickled egg again and it's still winking at me!" Byron hovered back to the boys with refills. As he lowered the drinks onto the table he surprised Vince by saying, "Sir, may I be so bold as to enquire, what's the craziest thing you've ever done when you were, excuse my French, fucked-up?" "I dunno mate… probably sitting here and drinking this brain-damage brew with Chainsaw. I know it's not exactly Motley Crüe… or is it?

But that aside, how come the sausages on that bloke's plate have tattoos? And why has that babe's pasty grown legs and is running around the bar trying to ponce a ciggie? And…why does that fuckin' pickled egg keep winking at me?" The vampire barman remained silent and flew off to point his pecker at the porcelain. Seeing this sent Chainsaw spastic and he started shaking uncontrollably. "Vince…" he stammered, "have you ever drawn a picture of a journalist passing out in his own puke?" "Why, Chain?" "BAROOGAHGAHGAH!" SPLAT! Suffering a fit of the shakes himself, but forever the consumptive professional, Satan's finest immediately pulled a pad and pencil from his holdall and started drawing the vomit and blood splattered form of his journo' buddy. But not for long, because he'd barely sketched an outline, when… SPLAT!

Several hours later… dawn broke and in the cold, hard light of day, the hung-over berserkers groaned and attempted to lift their heads. Heads that felt as though Oppenheimer was testing atom bombs inside them. The pain was one thing, but what followed next was something altogether harsher. Chainsaw was the first to prise open his eyelids. "Vince! Vince!" he screamed, holding his battered head so it didn't split down the middle. "What the fuck happened last night?" "We both passed out in your steaming spew is what happened matey boy," said Vince, his voice little more than a whisper. "No!" Chainsaw screamed again. "What happened to The Deliverance?" Vince finally opened his eyes and they almost flew from their sockets. He and Chainsaw were sitting in what may have once been a pub, but was now dusty old derelict ruins. The guys looked at each other in astonishment, then Chainsaw said, "Fuck this shit, we're out of here!"

Chain was already half way back to the van when Vince suddenly grabbed his gut and doubled up in obvious agony. "What's up?" Chainsaw shrieked. "I'm going to…" "BAROOGAHGAHGAH!" A stream of the bad stuff shot from Vince's mouth and splattered over his boots. He looked down at the mess and stared in shock. Floating on top of the gelatinous, diced-carrot infested, steaming gloop was a pickled egg. Puzzled, he was just about to wave Chainsaw back to see it, when…it winked at him! "AAARRRGGGHHH!!!" The End?

POSTER ART

The art of the rock poster had a big boom with the hippies and psychedelia until that style was swept away with the advent of punk in the 1970s. In more recent times, the likes of Frank Kozik revived the art with posters that promoted the band and brought a collectors market forward.

Nowadays, the visual possibilities seem endless with over fifty years of rock'n'roll culture to draw on. I like to mix it all up and include custom cars, tattoos, gothic skulls and all my all time fav, horror comic imagery. Hunting for cool fonts is a constant search. You get the best out of them by manipulating and twisting them to your own needs. I often draw my own embellishments on each letter to make them unique. All those years spent up a ladder sign writing seems to have paid off and I'm afraid to say that I'm sadly one of those fellas that can talk for hours about the variations on the shape of a letter 's'. Still hate 'k' though!

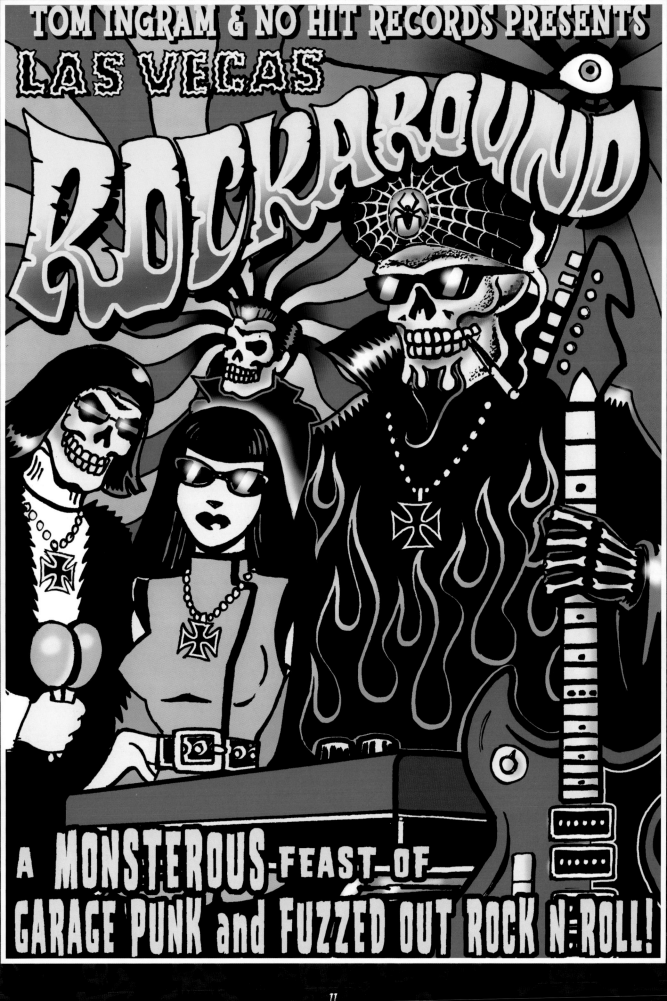

Posterpop have been instrumental in bringing low brow art to thousands of kids skate boards and guitars...and just about anything else that you can tag with a sticker! They've been a cool company to work for and did a great job of organizing my first exhibition in Los Angeles. There's plans for another show in 2006 and we'll also be putting something together for Viva Las Vegas Rockabilly Weekend. For more information regarding their vast range of stickers, posters and T-shirts, check out www.posterpop.com

WILDCAT

Wildcat are the main distributors for the Vince Ray Experience range of merchandize. They're famous for producing a vast range of body jewellery and some really cool silver skull rings that make me play the guitar slower than ever. The biggest one is about the size of an egg! Personally, the only thing I would have pierced is a sausage before I put it under the grill; I'm too much of a weed when it comes to needles. I like to see how other people put body art together though, combining metal, tattoos and vast amounts of personal bravery!

We started work together on a range of posters to promote Wildcat and I was kept busy with a commission for over fifteen paintings, some of which were included in the first book. This time round, we've included some of the t-shirt designs made specifically for the Wildcat catalogue and there is another set in production.

The Wildcat shop in Brighton has been a venue for book signings in the past and we usually get the band to play the night before. This leaves me hung-over and smelling of booze and cigarettes the following day whilst I sign books and get peoples names wrong. I once heard that a girl said, she'd met Vince Ray and he smelt really bad. I took that as a compliment of course...it takes years to achieve this patina!

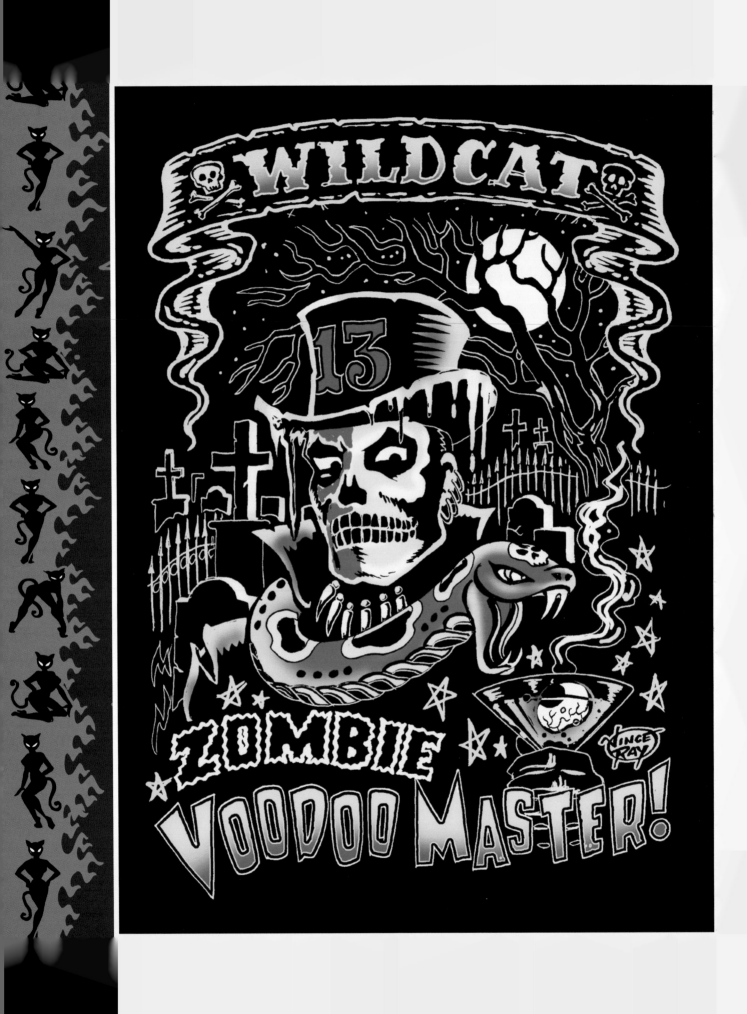

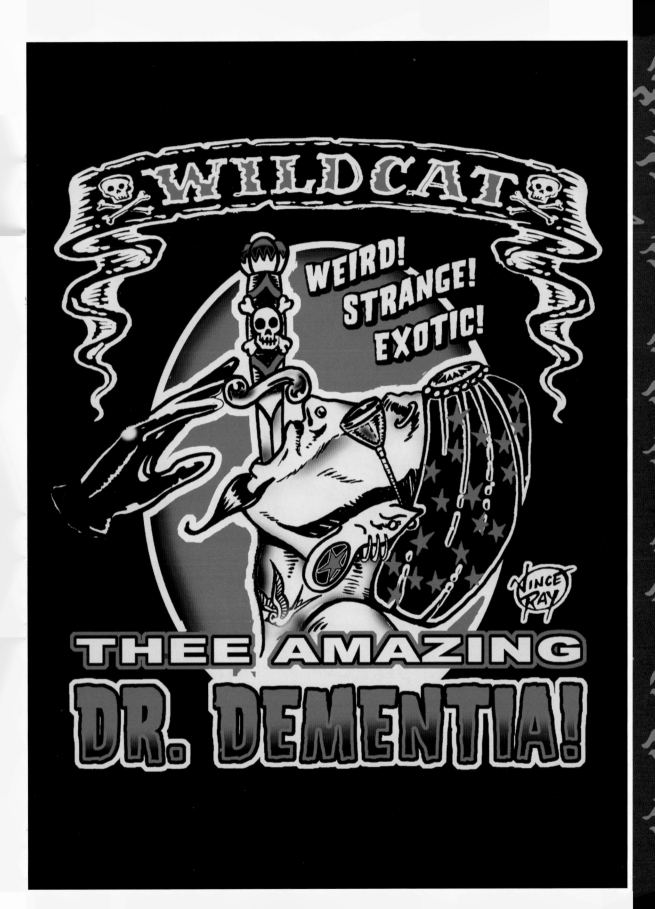

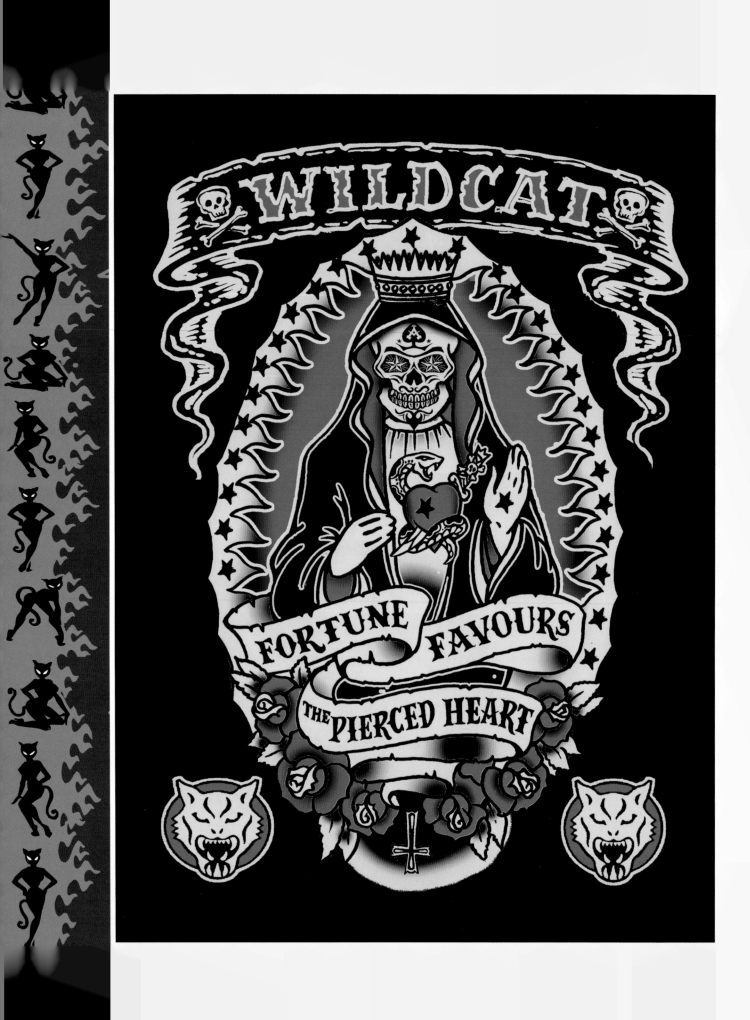

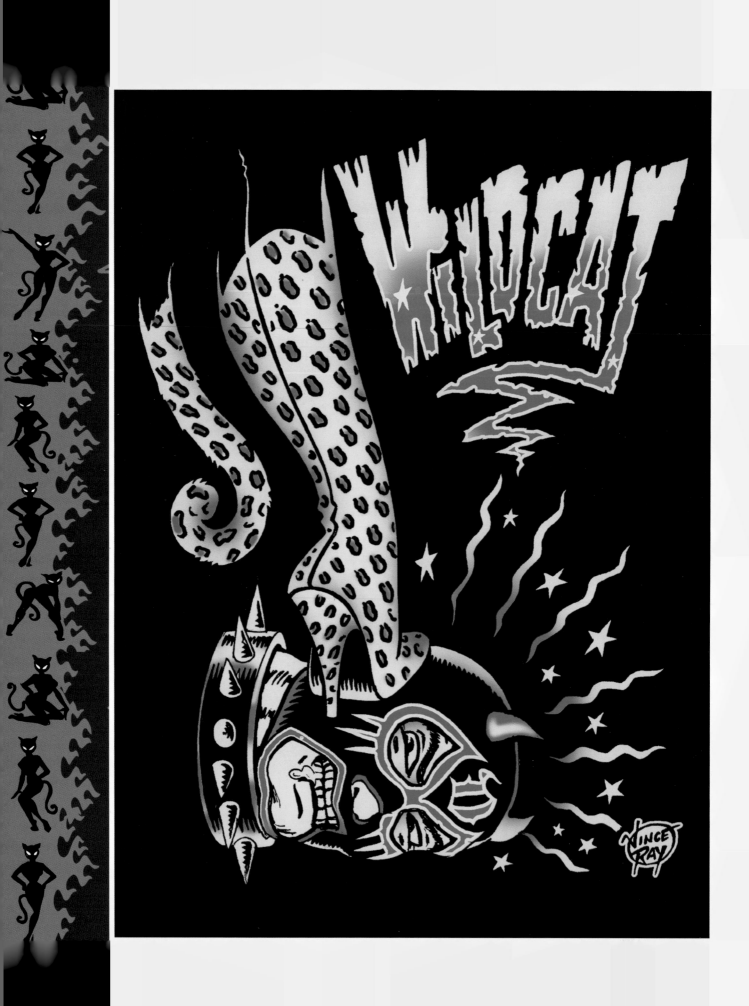

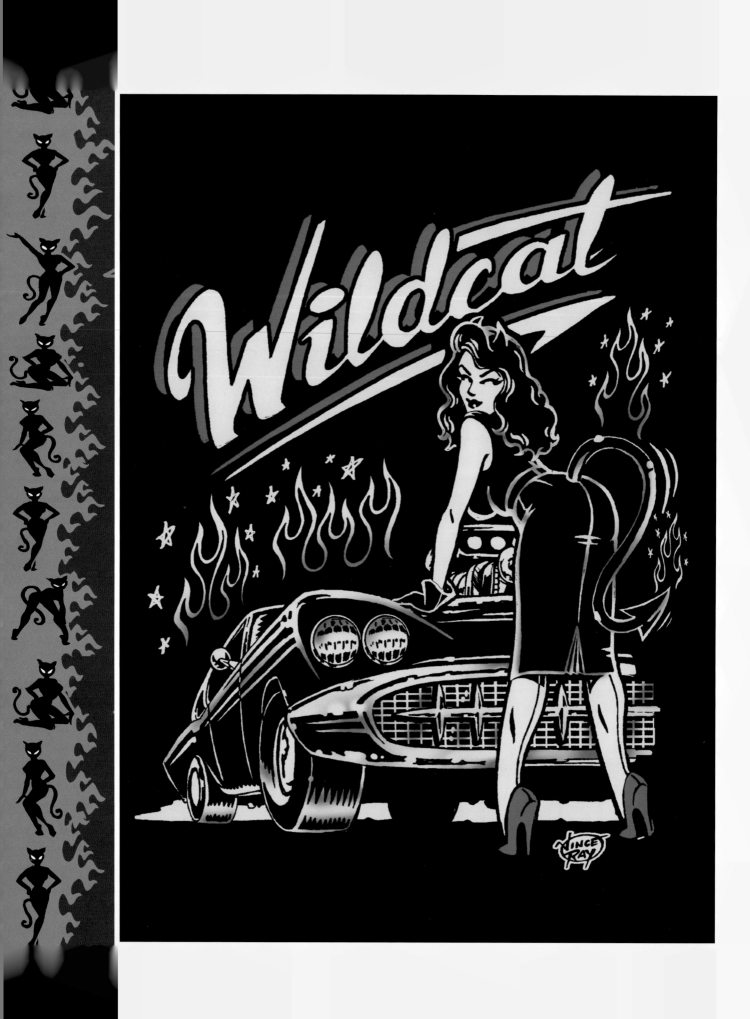

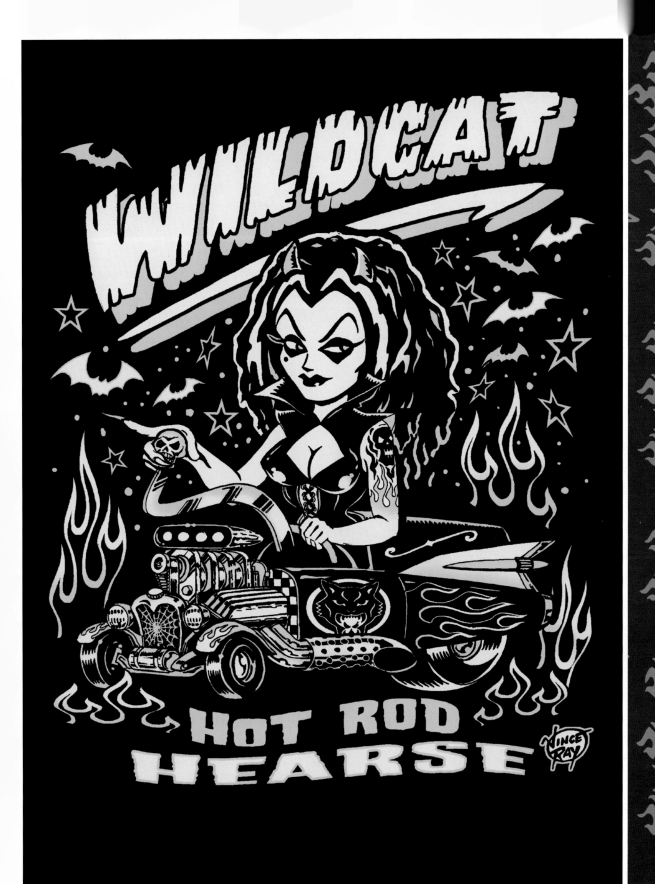

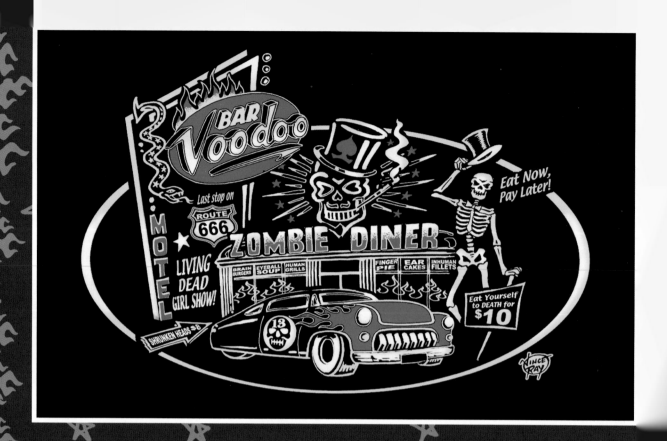

KILLED MY WIFE ABOUT
HALF PAST EIGHT...

SHOT HER IN THE FRONT PORCH
WITH MY BIG 38.

13

I CALLED HER TWIN SISTER
AROUND ABOUT NINE...

TOLD HER
EVERYTHING WAS
GONNA BE JUST
FINE...

CUNT

WOMAN
KILLER
BLUES...

RECORD COVERS

It is always a blast to design a record cover for a band I've always liked. I specialize in the areas of horror rock, psychobilly and punk rock'n'roll. Some bands have strong ideas about what they want and other times the brief is quite loose and I'm left up to my own devices to use my creativity and interpret their music and image as I feel it. Working to a brief can be tricky, as there also has to be room for an artist to bring something of himself to it.

Sometimes a job comes along and I'm left scratching my head trying to determine how we can bring the idea to life. But hey, I enjoy that challenge and often the best ideas come from tricky starts.

Occasionally, folks monkey around with things after they are delivered which usually bugs me. The client has to be happy and I make sure of that and never consider the job over with until they are.

Perhaps one day we'll do a Vince Ray colouring-in book!

I work mainly in Photoshop using scanned line drawings, adding the colour and shading on the computer. Unfortunately, this technology, which is great most of the time, means there is less and less hand-finished work on paper. I do try to keep a hand-drawn feeling and try avoid the image looking too computer generated.

© Anya Raucous

THE ADVENTURES OF THE LONG TALL TEXANS

ROCKABILLY

THE LONG TALL TEXANS · ADVENTURE

1. [unknown]
2. [unknown]
(m...)
3. DA... ...AVING FUN
(ian r... ...erter)
4. GET YOUR FEET OUTTA MY SHOES
(unknown)
5. NO MORE RUNNING AWAY
(mark denman)
6. IT REALLY DOESN'T BOTHER ME
(gary-castleman)
7. I'VE SEEN HER
(mark denman)
8. JAP SONG
(texans)
9. POORMANS POISON
(mark denman)
10. SAY WHEN
(john watts)
11. WHY DID YOU LIE TO ME
(gary-castleman)
12. YOU DON"T WANT ME
(gary-castleman)

THE LONG TALL TEXANS

THE LONG TALL TEXANS

ADVENTURE

LA ROCKA

#1 Hot-rod Shirt (back)

#2 Voodoo Shirt

KUSTOM SHOP

HOT RODS

La Rocka (Johnsons) were a legendary company who helped clothe thousands of rockabillies, mods and rockers from the seventies onwards. These shirts were distributed by an American company and are now collectors' items as they are no longer in production. Elsewhere in this book, you'll see examples of t-shirt designs that La Rocka still manufactures today. From time to time, the mad bad beatnik Mr Johnson himself, can be seen scootering through the wilds of Barnes Common.

#1 Hot-rod Shirt (front)

#3 Tiki Shirt

THAT SHIRT IS A
KNOCKOUT

#4 Surfers Shirt

#5 Fabluous
Las Vegas
(front)

#7 Lucky
Tattoo Shirt

#5 Fabluous
Las Vegas
(back)

#6 Go-kat-go
Shirt

June 6 1966   Issue 666

Voodoo News

THE CURSE OF THE VOODOO GUITAR!

LIZARD EYES sat like a magpie on a telegraph wire, gazing lazily at the customer who was showing him a creased photo of Blind Bullfrog Broonsey playing a cheap guitar. The stranger said he had the instrument, the exact same one as in the photo. He wished to sell it as he said the time had come for the guitar to find a new home. Lizard Eyes stroked his chin doubtfully as he examined the contents of the worn leather-bound case. It looked like the worms had been feasting for a while on the rotting swamp ash guitar body. He doubted it would ever play again, but for whatever reason, agreed to take it on for sale or return. Lizard Eye turned to reach for his receipt book but stopped when he heard the bell over the door ring. The shop was empty except for the two-tailed cat, hissing and spitting at the door. He began to think there was something amiss about the stranger. Couldn't put his finger on it. Maybe it was the way he cast no shadow, was dressed head to foot in red and had those two pointy horns on his brow. Kinda smelt of sulphur too.

Johnny bought the guitar for ten bucks from the man with lizard eyes and a cat with two tails. Little did he know that the guitar would cost him everything he owned in this life…and the hereafter! His wife hated it. They were broke and he'd spent the rent money on an old guitar with knots in the rusted strings strings where they'd busted. When Johnny was drunk, he'd stamp his foot and holler like John Lee Hooker and beat a primitive rhythm on the stupid guitar. Betty May thought it sounded like a train rolling backwards, then falling off a cliff into the smoldering pools of the Labria Tar Pits. She once prised the guitar from the putty like grip of her stoned husband and threw it onto the porch, hitting a chicken and killing it stone dead. Betty threw a really big shoe at it and went to bed.

Next day, Johnny was gone and the dead chicken was lying in the bed next to Betty May. Something white was dribbling from the egg duct. Johnny was weird like that, but she'd add a few spices of her own and boil it up anyway, just 'cos they were poor. She waited all day. She played the radio and made one good bra out of two worn out ones and painted her toe nails for Johnny so they'd look like a row of pretty cherries. When a hollering came from the porch, she hopped over to find Johnny dressed head to foot in a silver lamé suit. He had diamond

rings on every finger and alligator skin boots as big as boats…and an evil grin!

Blind Bullfrog Broonsey was a long gone blues player. He'd died penniless and legend had it that he'd been buried in an unmarked grave with his one and only possession–a busted old red guitar. White middle class blues aficionados had spent many years and a small fortune collecting scratched old records and memorabilia of Blind Bullfrog. The holy grail was that red guitar, but no one had been able to find the grave and confirm the sorry contents. As to how Lizard Eyes came by it, he wouldn't tell.

Johnny had been on his way back to the pawn shop to return the guitar, unaware of the value of the lost treasure packed underneath his arm. It was just a shitty old thing that had gotten him his ass busted by his wife. He'd get that rent money back even if he had to pull Lizard Eyes face off and wipe his butt with it. The day was hot and as Johnny passed the Dimebuster Diner and Grill, he smacked his parched lips in need of a beer. At first, he was the only customer, sitting alone on the torn leatherette of a bench seat. He stared thoughtlessly at the guitar opposite as if he was on a useless date. The silence was broken by the rasp of a pack of cards as two expert hands shuffled the pack. Johnny looked over to the next table and raised an eyebrow in admiration as the red suited man deftly handled the cards. A few minutes later, they were playing poker and Johnny was smiling to himself thinking of how the odds were stacked incredibly in his favour. There was a big pile of money, more than he'd ever seen right under his nose. And all this stranger wanted was that old red guitar! Well, there was another part of the deal, but Johnny had never believed in any heaven or hell and the idea that he'd even got a soul to sell was plain hocus pocus to him. If this guy was some kind of preacher, he'd just play along a while 'till he could make an exit with every pocket stuffed with those crisp green notes.

Johnny never got to become a legend, but he did get the mansion. High on the hills

of Baton Rouge on the outskirts of New Orleans, the towers of La Ronez stood like two black and broken fangs on the hillside. Betty May had big plans when they moved into the 17th century house, derelict since the civil war. It was going to be like Gone with the Wind, but with a happy ending. The only thing that had come true was that Johnny really didn't give a damn. When a

poor boy gets rich in the twinkling of an eye, his simple mind gets twisted and he turns to all the evil pleasures that he could never afford before. Betty May slept all day whilst Johnny lay beside her in the bible black darkness. Just a slither of light through the shutters helped him guide the needle to create the next track mark, another carriage on the long black train to that dark land where he could dream whilst still awake. His wife lived another life by night, one which he never asked about anymore. He'd watch silently as she put on that rich whore dress and bouffant wig. A car horn would sound in the drive and she'd swing those weighted hips to the door with a mocking swagger. She'd come home in the morning without one or both of her shoes. Once, Johnny had asked about him. All she said was that he always wore a smart red suit and smelt like spent matches.

On the sixth day of the sixth month in 1966, Johnny woke, wet from head to foot in an evil fever. It was forty eight degrees and raining that day and his head was splitting like thunder. Betty May should be home by now, dribbling into her pillow with that ever present hangover. Johnny did something that was rare at that time. He spoke, telling his wife about the hellish

dream that he'd just had. For seven days he'd lay deep in a coffin with the worms and the soil. Nothing moved, not his arms or his legs or his skinny neck. Seven days that seemed like a silent eternity, until eventually he thought he heard a distant scrapping. For the first time in ten years, he thought about that poker game. Johnny thought about heaven and hell. He thought about being saved, maybe in this life or the hereafter. The scrapping got louder with each prayer. Someone was digging for him, digging frantically just above the coffin lid, someone was gonna save him! The rhythmic shovelling of earth above him ceased for a moment. Johnny lay frozen as the silence returned for a moment until a thunderous crack split the coffin lid in two. The moonlight burned his shrouded eyes, eyes that had stared ceaselessly into oblivion for seven days. There was the moon, framed by the twisted gnarled branches in the overgrown cemetery. And there were those red sheet ripping stilettos. The mesh of her stockings blurred in his vision as Johnny looked up and over those swaying hips, up to that big black torpedo bra that he liked so much.

It was Betty May for sure, her raven black hair covering her face as her breath came in short hot pants. But Betty May was not alone. A big dark shadow of a man stood behind her, eyes glowing as red as two poker tips. Betty May rolled her head back and sighed, leaning back into the darkness. She raised her arms, holding the shovel like an executioners axe in two leather gloved hands. But the shovel was red and guitar shaped with broken strings and switches. For a moment, a breeze parted her hair and Johnny saw the faint glimmer of a smile cross her lips as she swung the instrument through the air with the ease of a seasoned wood chopper. Thunder broke and split the silence of the graveyard along with Johnnys head as he awoke, stumbling for words to describe the nightmare.

Betty May? Maybe she was sleeping and hadn't heard a word of the dark tale. He thought he heard her sigh or maybe laugh a little. Johnny's arm felt heavy, swollen and blue as he stretched over to feel towards her side of the bed. The sheets were wet and cold. Something was sticking to his fingers,

something like bloody chicken feathers. He tried to pull his hand back, but wires bit into the tendons beneath his flesh. There was a neck, broken and splintered. Johnny couldn't scream. The shadow on the wall was fading fast, but he just managed to make out the shape of an inverted guitar like the cross over a tombstone. The shaft of the cross was plunged deep into Betty May's bossom and Johnny wasn't dreaming.

T-SHIRTS

T-shirt art has probably kept me busier over the years than anything else. It's something that just won't go away, and each week a couple of commissions come in from bands, record and clothing companies. You may rightly notice that generally, I work in black, red and cream with the occasional experimental green or purple for horror or psychobilly-themed designs.

The red and cream combination seems to always have that vintage vibe, not too fancy for the tough guys and yet punchy enough to be seen in a crowd. I like to keep the design with an open feel, not too boxed-in unless that's the specific aim.

A few years ago, the Vince Ray Experience company released a design that said BITCH in big twisted letters alongside a foxy looking gal wielding a whip. We sold boxes of those, it seemed to come at a time when girls were getting stuck into some attitude and kind of said that they were in control and not to be messed with. For the record, we also had a design that said SLAVE to even things out, but we did not sell quite so many of those!

VOODOO CHOP SHOP

Custom Parts

© Dragstrip

dragSTER

★ HOTROD, DEVIL ROCK! ★

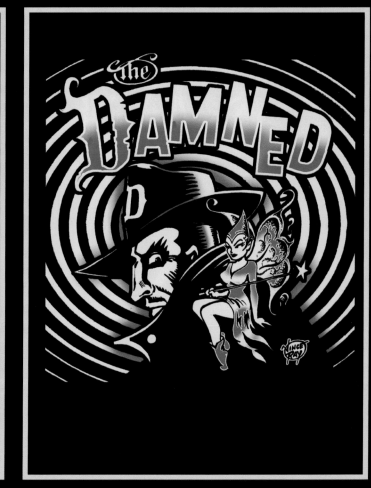

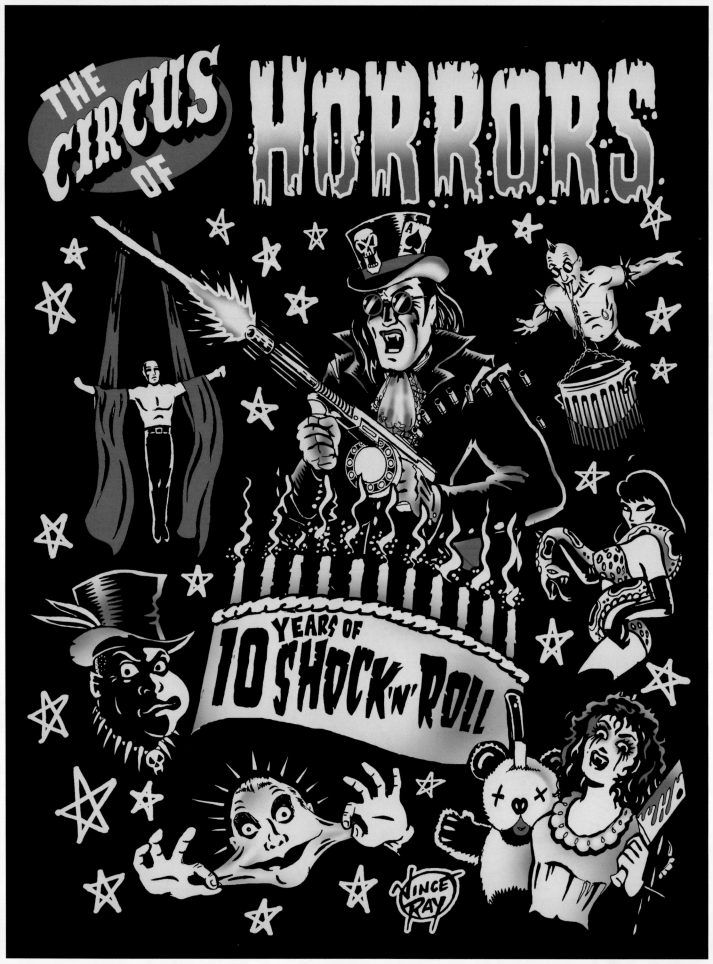

GRETSCH

6120 BLUES

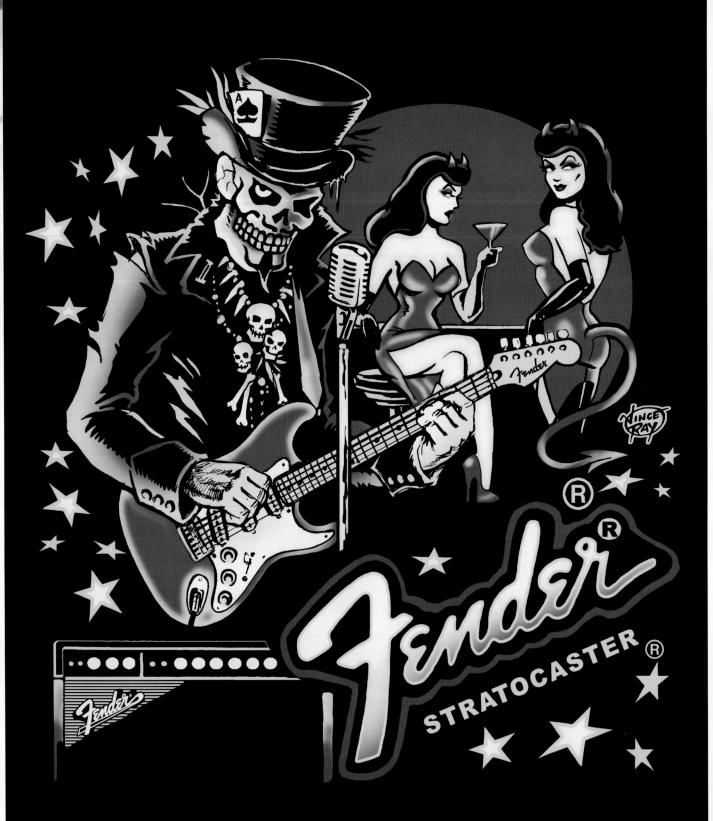

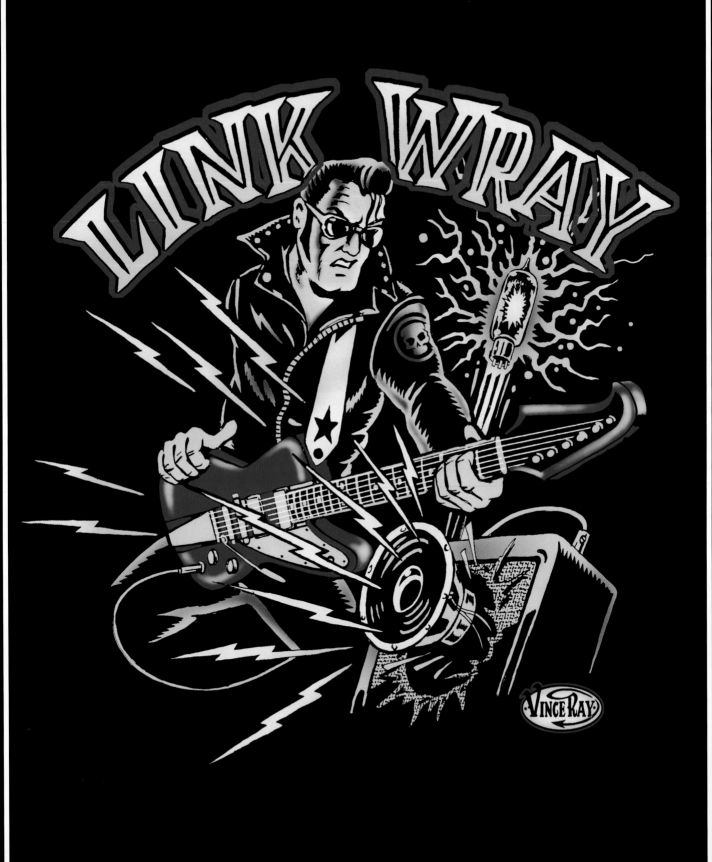

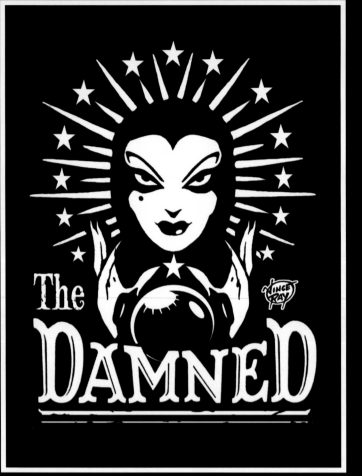

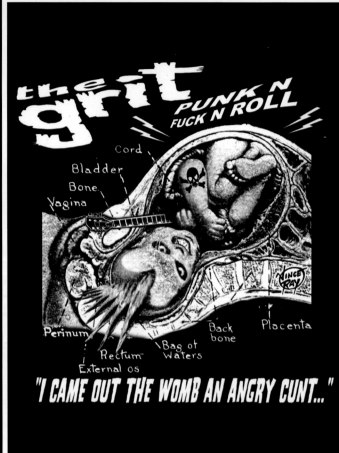

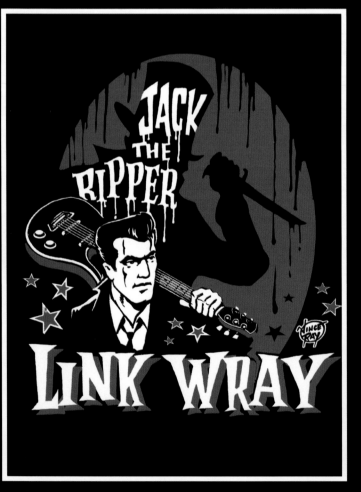

MISCELLENEOUS

Here's a section of work that we couldn't find a home for elsewhere...hand bags, key rings, logos, painted guitars and weird stuff! Roebuck were a great company who came up with some cool ideas like the voodoo drum handbag. I bought my Mum one for Christmas but she said she couldn't take it to midnight mass, dunno why?!

It's always good to get a brief for an idea that makes me want to get home and start work on it right away and look forward to the whole process that leads to the finished product.

I've always painted my guitars, it seems like a natural thing to do as well as playing them. An instrument becomes personalized when you play it — the chords and riffs bring it to life. To customize a guitar visually feels like part of the same process to me. Here's a top tip: Get down your Dad's garage now, pop open a can of black and red paint and start painting, Kids!

The artwork for the Gretsch guitars was a dream come true as I'm sadly obsessed with those old boxes! I'm more interested in collecting them than paying the rent so in the past was happy to swap guitars for artwork. There is always the chance that you'll see me on a street corner soon with ten guitars and no home! Luckily there are more painted guitar commissions in the pipeline...guess I won't starve and Miss Katie won't brain me for not bringing home the rent!

THE VINCENT RAZORBACKS

VINCE RAY
LORD FORD
DISCO DOM
THE GAFF

www.vincentrazorbacks.com

WHAT ABOUT THAT ROBERT JOHNSON HEY? Apparently, he walked into a juke joint sometime in the 1940's, tried to jam with the warty old blues guys and played like a twat and made a total dick of himself. Legend has it that he returned six months later, performed like a demon and blew the roof of with his nifty licks. Someone said he must have sold his soul to the devil at the crossroads in exchange for his gift.

Fair enough! I thought I'd give it a go and read everything I could about the crossroads and how it works. Here's one version that I tried. At midnight on the seventh day of the seventh month, I took my guitar down to the nearest crossroads and waited.

The story goes that a mysterious stranger would appear, take the guitar, tune it, and then hand it back (don't take your chromatic tuner with you or he'll get real miffed!). Sure enough, on the stroke of midnight, a dark shadow of a man did appear and take the guitar... and then ran like fuck and jumped on a 73 bus.

Maybe that was part of the legend that I'd missed. I went home, picked up another guitar, and started to play. Amazingly , I still played like a twat!

Apparently, there's a *devil's chord* and it's meant to be a flattened fifth (all musical anoraks will know this). Jimi Hendrix used this chord at the beginning of Purple Haze but Paganini employed it hundreds of years ago and was banned from playing it by the church. This chord makes God go mental and kick off with the Virgin Mary, whilst baby Jesus shits himself. Make sure you play this chord wherever possible.

Volume 13...Selling your soul to the devil? It's been a busy year. Someone was telling me recently how the number 13 really IS unlucky. I don't really believe in all that stuff, but since we decided to call the second album *Volume 13*, the project seemed to get trampled to death by the devil herself in her highest red stilettos. It started as an offer you can't refuse...big Japanese record company say "Go into the studio, record for weeks, get drunk, spend loads of dosh and we'll pay for EVERYTHING!"

Well, what would you do? Same as us, I guess, pretend to rehearse, sit in the pub and boast about the imminent rock star status that awaits in Japan. We'd pretty much finished the whole thing when Japanese record company goes BUST big time, leaving the Vincent Razorbacks offering to clean the recording studio bogs for a year till the debt was paid...do you know how many toilets you have to clean to pay back half a million?

Fortunately, there was light at the end of the tunnel (but there was a train coming!).

Time now for the awards ceremony acceptance speech: "I'd like to thank both my arms for being by my side and all my fingers because I've always been able to count on them.... and Howard Raucous too!"

Raucous Records took up the deal, spanked the devil, and sent her off on her way with the debt paid. Thus, *Volume 13* rose from the ashes and will be available from all good record shops. Just don't play it backwards.

Who the fuck wants to be a rock star anyway? There's a level of 'success' (way above our toilet tour status) where some dumb young record company jerk arranges your whole life for you. They decide where you go, what you should and worst case how you should sound. All your mates are chucked out the band 'coz they're too

drunk and can't play. They wheel in some super duper muso's who know all the right poses. I promise you this; your band will become shite, I have seen it happen loads of times. I like the level we're at. It's a war between the band and the audience and you win when they get to fall in a sweaty pile at the end of the gig. If you lose and they hate you, that's even better.

"Thanks a lot and fuck off!"…Van, kebab, motorway and hangover, is always a winner. If you're not old, twisted and bitter like me then you've got a lot to look forward to. I blame that cunt that nicked me guitar on the 73 bus, in fact I'm not even sure it was the devil anyway.

I can't finish this section without mentioning my brothers-in-arms. These are the drunks who know all the Vincent Razorbacks songs backwards (and sometimes even plays them backwards).

Lord Ford: Taught to play guitar by aliens and does a mean UFO impersonation. An eerie man with the ability to play anything you can mention. Once asked him to play 'On A Far Off Hill' and he did – in Devon – we could still hear him in London.

West End Gaff: Earl of Soho and the world's loudest drummer. To stand next to him on stage is like being in World War 3. We used to have two Go-Go Girls but Gaff ate them when the pies ran out. Can also drive a van asleep.

Disco Dom: "The man with the funk in his fingers." Actually, he can play really well but we tie three of his fingers together when he plays with us. To see this man dance is something else…whiskey in one hand, eight cigarettes and two transvestites in the other…"Fuck, it's a bloke!"

Louie Ville: The angry cunt…even wrote a song to prove it called *I Came Out the Womb an Angry Cunt* which he sings in his other band, The Grit. Still young and bendy enough to jump into an audience and rub his guitar on the noses of anyone not enjoying the gig.

…and last but not least **Shotgun Andy** who drives over tourists in Leicester Square.

Photos by Paul Xerox from JACK THE RIPPER promo made by
www.thecryandthechainsaw.co.uk

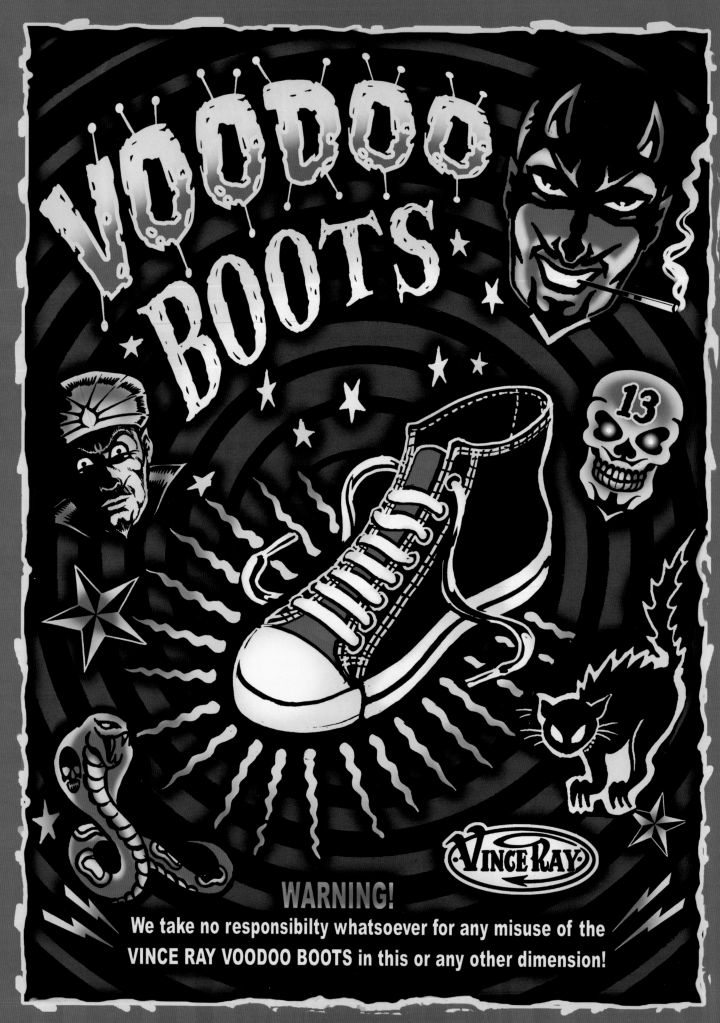

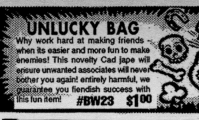